A FUN BOOK OF NUMBERS

MAGIC MONKE'.

This edition published 1992
by BCA by arrangement with
WAYLAND (PUBLISHERS) LTD

CN 5571

First published in 1990 by
Firefly Books Limited
61 Western Road, Hove
East Sussex BN3 1JD, England

© Copyright 1990 Firefly Books Limited

© Copyright Neil Morris (text) Peter Stevenson (artwork)

Editor: Francesca Motisi

Typeset by DP Press Limited, Sevenoaks, Kent
Printed and bound in Belgium by Casterman S.A.

A FUN BOOK OF NUMBERS

MAGIC MONKEY

Written by Neil Morris
Illustrated by Peter Stevenson

BCA

LONDON · NEW YORK · SYDNEY · TORONTO

Monkey lives in the children's room with all the other toys. But he is magic. When no one is there, he comes out of the toybox and monkeys around.

4

Magic Monkey loves numbers. One day he counts
all the things in the children's room.

One doll's house.
Pity there isn't a monkey house too!

1

Two beds. The top bunk is Gemma's, and Timmy sleeps in the bottom bunk.

2

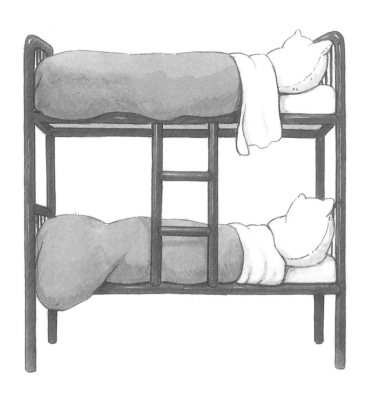

On the top bunk Monkey sees three bears.
He thinks it's time for a rest.

3

Here are four balls.
Who wants to play catch with Magic Monkey?

Five dolls are having a tea party.
But they don't like Monkey joining in.

5

Monkey finds six crayons.
He draws a picture of Gemma and Timmy.

6

17

Then Monkey counts seven toy cars.
He takes them out of the garage
and makes a traffic jam.

7

19

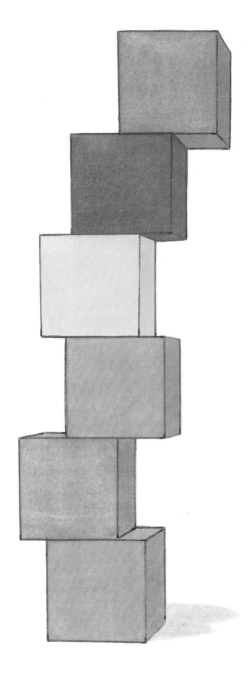

Here are eight building bricks.
Monkey builds a high tower. **8**
Watch out, it's toppling!

Nine marbles, all in a row.
Silly Monkey slips on them.

9

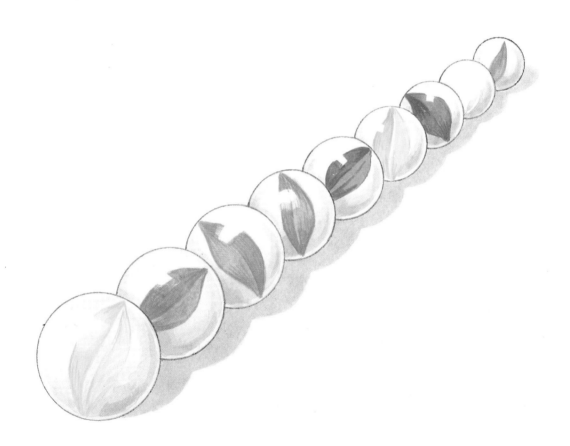

Here are ten books.
Magic Monkey reads his favourite story.

10

Suddenly Monkey hears a noise.
There's someone coming, but
there are too many footsteps to count.

Magic Monkey jumps back into the toy box.
Goodbye, Magic Monkey!

1 one

2 two

3 three

4 four

5 five

6 six

7 seven

8 eight

9 nine

10 ten

Notes for adults

Children who go to school already knowing how a book 'works' have a great deal of knowledge that will help them to make the entry into reading much easier. It is far more important to share a book with a child than to try to teach him/her to read. These books aim to introduce very young children to the world around them.

Before reading this book talk about the pictures on the cover. What does your child think the book is about? Talk about the title and point to the words. Tell him/her that all books are written by authors and often illustrated by a different person. Show them the names of the author and illustrator.

Before reading the story look through the book together and talk about the illustrations. Encourage the child to tell his/her own story to the pictures. This important pre-reading skill helps children to develop an understanding of the story that is essential to reading.

Do let the child hold the book and give him/her time to look at the pictures before talking about them. Adults often rush in with questions far too soon.

REMEMBER when looking at the pictures there is no 'right' or 'wrong' guess. Accept what the child suggests and add your own ideas. You will be bringing much more knowledge to the pictures but s/he may surprise you.

After reading the book let the child explore the book on his/her own. S/he may want to return to a favourite picture, retell the story to a special toy, or just turn the pages pretending to be a reader. A joy in books comes from being allowed to use them as the reader wishes and not necessarily as an adult would have them do.

Discussion points

Talking about the illustrations will help your child to get more from the story. Here are some suggestions for things to discuss. The numbers refer to the pages on which the illustrations appear.

MAGIC MONKEY

The numbers one to ten are presented in sequence in this story book. The last page acts as a reminder, with the numbers shown as numerals, words and objects. As you read the story, encourage the child to count with Monkey. Afterwards, you could add to the fun by helping the child play with numbers using toys and household objects. Make a counting book with cut-out magazine pictures, or start a collection (three of something, four of something else).

4/5 The children's room is very tidy. Where is Magic Monkey and why is he magic? Find all the toys in the room.

6 How many doors and chimneys has the doll's house? Count the windows. Why can't Monkey live in this doll's house?

9 What is Monkey doing? How many rabbits can you spot? Where would you rather sleep, in the top or the bottom bunk?

10 What are the bears wearing? Monkey's eyes are closed. Count all the open eyes!

13 How many balls do you play catch with? How many is Monkey playing with?

14 Has every doll got a bow? Count all the bows. Which doll do you like best?

15 Why don't the dolls want Monkey to join in? Count the cups and plates. What's Monkey balancing on his head? Would you invite Monkey to a tea party?

17 Monkey can draw two pictures at the same time! How does he do it?

19 How many red cars are in the traffic jam? Next time you are stuck in a traffic jam, count all the red cars.

21 How many bricks are toppling? Build your own tower and count the bricks. Is your tower higher than Monkey's?

25 Monkeys love bananas. Why do you think this is Monkey's favourite story, and what might the story be about?

26/27 Who messed up the room? Look back at the first page and compare the two pictures. When Monkey heard the footsteps, he quickly jumped back into the toybox. You can count noises too. Listen out for footsteps (there were too many for Magic Monkey to count), a ball when it bounces, a clock when it chimes the hour, or a dripping tap.